PS
3505
.U976
W4
C.1
CUTLER
WEST WIND RISES
3.00
PS
3505
.U976
W4
AUTHOR
Cutle
TITLE
West
DATE LOANED
D1057888
3 29 72
1972

A WEST WIND RISES

Also by Bruce Cutler

THE YEAR OF THE GREEN WAVE   1960

A WEST WIND RISES

By Bruce Cutler

Illustrated by

David E. Bernard

UNIVERSITY OF NEBRASKA PRESS · LINCOLN

Portions of this poem have appeared in *The Kansas Magazine, Midwest, The Midwest Quarterly, Poetry, Prairie Schooner, The Wichita Eagle and Beacon,* and in the anthology *Kansas Renaissance.*

Library of Congress catalog card number 62-14661

Manufactured in the United States of America

David and John

We cannot escape history. . . . No personal significance or insignificance can spare one or another of us. The fiery trial through which we pass will light us down in honor or dishonor to the latest generation.

—Abraham Lincoln

FOREWORD

On May 19, 1858, a party of slaveowners and their sympathizers rode without warning into a hamlet called Trading Post in the Kansas Territory and seized eleven Free State settlers. They then took the men to an isolated point near the Missouri-Kansas border where they shot them down and fled. Immediately, a brigade was organized by James Montgomery, the leader of Free State forces in the area, but it had little success in tracking down the members of the raiding party, all of whom had fled across the border into Missouri.

The Raiders were led by Charles Hamelton, a Georgian who came to the Kansas Territory in 1855 in order to help make it a slave state. Hamelton was accompanied on the raid by some two dozen other Kansans and Missourians, including his brother Alvin; Fort Scott Brockett, himself the leader of raiding parties on other occasions; a man called Hubbard, known for his border brawling; two brothers named Yealock; Aaron Cordell, a friend of Hamelton's; a man named Matlock; and William Griffith, a member of the band who in 1863 was captured, tried, and executed for his part in the Massacre.

Of the Free State settlers captured by the Raiders, the first was a man named Wing who was in charge of a sawmill on the Marais des Cygnes River. For some unknown reason, he and another man named G. B. Andrews were released. Others captured were John Campbell, a clerk in the Trading Post store who was killed; Reverend B. L. Read, missionary to the Indians, shot and seriously wounded; Patrick Ross, from Fort Lincoln on the Osage River, seized with Read and killed; William A. Stillwell from Indiana, killed; Amos Hall, taken from his sickbed, shot and wounded; William Colpetzer, killed; Michael Robertson, formerly of Effingham, Illinois, killed; Robertson's houseguest, Charles Snider, shot and wounded; William Hairgrove and his son Amos, former Georgians who had voted "free" in a Territorial election, seriously wounded; and Austin W. Hall, brother of Amos Hall, nearly blind with an acute infection of his eyes, who escaped injury.

A few days later, a stunned American public received the news of what quickly became known as the "Marais des Cygnes Massacre." Charles Tomlinson, writing in *Kansas in 1858,* purports to have sent the original dispatch to the New York *Tribune*; he had ridden to the site of the massacre from Westport Landing (Kansas City) the day after it occurred. After his report was published, public opinion was inflamed against the South for what seemed to be the wholly unprovoked, savage, and coldly premeditated nature of the shooting. Whittier's poem, "Marais du Cygne," appeared later in 1858 in the *Atlantic Monthly* and was widely reprinted.

After the Civil War ended, and throughout the rest of the nineteenth century, a few Kansas historians like Andreas and Connelly painstakingly gathered more information on the incident and the events that led up to it. William Ansell Mitchell, the author of a history of Linn County, Kansas, went even further into an examination of the personalities and historical forces involved. Another important source of information was an unpublished thesis, "Border Warfare in Southeastern Kansas, 1856-1859" by George M. Welch (University of Kansas, 1938). Mr. and Mrs. John H. Morse of Mound City, Kansas, were helpful in gathering and evaluating source materials, and additional facts were given me by Mr. Amos H. Hall of Paola, Kansas. I am particularly grateful to Walter Merrill for his encouragement in this project; and I thank the University of Wichita for the respect and freedom it accords its faculty members, including those who write, paint, and compose.

The narrative that follows is a dramatic reconstruction of what happened at Trading Post on that May nineteenth. Since it is a poem and not "history," I have not encumbered it with footnotes and the usual historical apparatus. I have left out a few of the men who were involved—Alvin Hamelton, for example—because I felt their presence in the poem would be unnecessarily confusing; and I have created some wholly fictional characters—like Hardin Sheek—who were not present in the annals of the event, but who surely were there in spirit. By doing this, I carried the narrative beyond the hard skeleton of fact into the vulnerable tissue of probability; if it is blemished, lay it to me, the translator, and not to the people who lived and died—not for the dust of the museum, but for the land that one day would be ours.

Bruce Cutler

CONTENTS

Foreword vii

Dispatch to the New York *Tribune* 3

James Montgomery Builds His House in Kansas 15

The Meeting at Jackson's Store 27

Miriam Nickell's Letter to Her Mother 39

Statement by the Reverend Mr. B. L. Read 51

The Marriage of Lily Stillwell 63

The Battle at Snyder's Forge 75

The Massacre 87

The Hanging of William Griffith 97

I

DISPATCH TO THE NEW YORK *TRIBUNE*

DISPATCH TO THE NEW YORK TRIBUNE

Trading Post, Kansas Territory
May 20, 1858

The shortest route to Trading Post lay down
in bottom ground where oak-roots veined the
banks
and soft alluvium of swelling streams;
then rose through sinuous stands of sycamore,
through bursting crimson maple-blossoms
and hillside altitudes of wild-apple
flowering in prodigal disuse. How Spring
had whet that air to sweetness! I traveled
armed, in company with Free State men who said
they rode to join Montgomery's guerrillas.
Closemouthed, civil, each seemed to manifest
his own dissimulation of intent,
but it was evident they'd settle up
the audit of a massacre in blood.

Descending to the ford, our horses slowed
and walked pastern-deep in gumbo along

the broad meanders of Marais des Cygnes.
She ran chocolate with mud that day. And deep.
To South, a rapids shoaled with limbs and roots
pushed whitecaps in the tide
as though the Cheyenne chief and his beloved
Nanonie played below,
surfaced as swans, or slowly spread their wings
to soar into the warm and depthless hemisphere
above.

We had to drive our horses hard across.

Trading Post was half a mile beyond.
The sod and log-roofed buildings lay out low
and ruinous. So desolate the scene,
at first I failed to note new signs of violence.
Horses filled the lean-to's;
guerrillas camped about the trading shack.
Entering, I discerned a plank table,
lighted by tallow, crowded all about
with visages that bore the Massachusetts
stamp, their eyes as clear as quartz is blue,
their beards untrimmed, it seemed, since Cincinnati.
One man beckoned, wiped a dish, and bade me eat.

His name was Eli Snyder. His hands as large
as hams were grizzled over, backs and palms;
blacksmith by trade, he was a Free State man.
Journalist, he said, *the men of Trading Post*
were Free Soil in politics; primitive
in character; inoffensive, in truth.
Peace men. Three years before, a certain Charles
Hamelton arrived from Georgia; his kin
came after him and helped construct a house
more fortified than most.
Softspoken eloquence, memory for names
made Hamelton a justice of the peace.
Freemen forgot he owned a dozen slaves.

By 1857, Emigrant Aid
had sent out steamboats full of Free State men
and James Montgomery rode the borders East:
as prospects of enslaving Kansas fell
the viper skin of Hamelton's deceit
peeled with his political power. Then
the man and border ruffian stood revealed
in true deformity.

His house became a fort and palisades.
The Judas band—Brockett, Hubbard, and all
manner of Missouri men—took rein,
burning, stealing, beating Free State men—
lighting down at night, long gone with the dawn
Missouri-bound across the water.

It is impossible to explain what hope
or desperation pricked the stallion flanks
of Hamelton's desires. He issued threats
against the lives of travelers; he compiled
lists of Free State men he marked for capture
and summary dispatch. Called *Captain* now,
hinting he led five score irregulars,
he commandeered horses from the settlements
all along Marais des Cygnes. By Spring
of 1858, good Free State men
rose up, and ringed his cedar palisades
with blazing pitch and steel of Sharps' rifles,
ordering him to leave forthwith. He did.
And rode six miles to Jackson's store, Missouri.
There, on 18 May, he met his men.
Are you for blood? he asked. They were. *Then ride*
with me tomorrow down Marais des Cygnes.
We'll settle with those bastards once for all.

Twenty-five agreed to strike the blow
for blood on Trading Post that day, when May
breezes played in the sycamores and oaks.

At nine o'clock on 19 May, the men
of Trading Post harrowed their furrows, felled
cedars, adzed a ridge-pole out of oak.
Clouds of dust arose from cattle droves.
Sun was opening the vaults of God's green
treasury, soft-yielding to the nipping hoe.
Women washed. A smell of smoke
and lye-soap shouldered among the trees
like sweet-armed incense, and children planted
peas.
A pilgrim village, washing out its hair
one May morning, well
might move a murderer to mind the voice
of natural compassion. But Hamelton
did not. As dark as winds that whip the arms
of mountain pines, his raiders swept around
Spy Mound. As sleep relaxed a baby's hand
cupped to the image of its mother's breast, they
burst
out of the timber, deadly as the Sioux.

Some gripped pistols. Others drew two-edged
border knives. They pulled young Johnny Campbell
and G. B. Andrews from the store; then
they toppled shelves. They sacked the calicoes
and bolts of crinoline, stuffed them inside
buffalo robes. Boots and shoes and cash,
such as it was, they split. The one named Hubbard
swore the settlers owed him high and wide,
their *lives* and *wives,* and searched for whiskey.
His mad
commander, meanwhile, ferreted the men
out of the fields and mill for hostages.
A William Stillwell happened upon the scene:
his buckboard became
the plunder wagon, and he a prisoner.
The settlers—pressed by horsemen, knocked down
and jeered—
were driven from their town. A missionary
crossed their trail; he too was seized and driven.
The black-boot Herod marked eleven men
for sacrifice, then went himself to take
the blacksmith Snyder, who threw him out
and shotgunned him. Raging with this defeat,

Hamelton drove his victims along
a grass ravine, lined them up five yards away,
and turned his guns upon them. The south wind
swept
along that smooth declivity; cottonwoods
soughed in the wind. The men who were con-
demned
stood bareheaded and unarmed upon the slope,
backs to the naked prairie that rose
a grassland roadway to the Otherwhere.

No one asked for mercy. A Free State man
said, *Gentlemen, if you intend to shoot*
then take good aim. One of the ruffians
broke away from line, but Hamelton swore
him back. The sense of triumph possessed,
climbed
as visibly upon his face as blood:
he raised his Colt, ordering his men to fire.
With the fall of firing pins, the charges blown,
ball and buckshot irrevocably dispatched,
the bodies fell awkwardly, spilling back,
pitching across the sod
boot to boot, arm to temple, slowly sinking
their stiffening fingers in the buffalo grass.
Hamelton said, *Be sure they all are dead.*

His men did not respond. A moment passed.
Tentative, a few dismounted and approached
the bodies. Stillwell lay face up, his breast
a sponge, killed by a double-barrel blast
of rodded pistol balls. *He's dead,* said one.
Then they began to kick the bodies,
roll them, searching for signs of life. When one
victim groaned, it was Hamelton who placed
his warm revolver to that ear and fired,
remarking as he did he'd always found
shots like that the surest he could make.
His men observed, but sickened inwardly.
They quickly stripped the bodies of their rings
and mounted. Working with haste, they over-
looked
what Free State men were still alive. Hamelton's
irregulars seemed to have had their fill
of back-shooting. In desultory file
they rode out of the long ravine, wending down
a rusty watercourse to the shade of trees.

Now I have seen the dead and consoled the few
survivors, I impatiently await
the imminent arrival of Montgomery
before we cross in force to open up
that abscess called *Missouri* for the murderers.

Meanwhile, the women slowly search the fields
for oxen standing, waiting with their plows;
they unknot the rawhide, lift off the yokes,
and bring them slowly home. Women ride
in ox-carts to the mouth of that ravine
where Stillwell's wagon stands, his grocery sacks
empty on the dashboard. From there, they walk
in shadows. Something tainted, sweet, begins
to infiltrate the air. The children weep,
not knowing why, and help to quench with tears
the venom of the curses that you hear
voiced by these guerrillas, waiting, waiting.
We all wait. But it will not be for long.
We know, if ever we were ignorant,
this *is the visage of that system known*
as slave, honest and undissimulate.
Reader: a territory large enough
to be a kingdom lies within its grasp,
the prairies, hills, rivers slowly blackening
under the shackles dragged by Africans!
Ride with us, that the seeds of freedom grow
to trunk and taproot from these ashes! Proclaim
in words broadcast to the living wind:
red oaks of justice root in Kansas soil!

II

JAMES MONTGOMERY BUILDS HIS HOUSE IN KANSAS

JAMES MONTGOMERY BUILDS HIS HOUSE IN KANSAS

1854-1858

Montgomery of Kentucky's Licking River
farmed his father's land and Mastered school.
Then, at thirty-nine, his inner ear
discerned a Leading voice: thereupon, he felled
a linden, dug it out, perched his wife
and sons precarious as owls inside
and set his course for Westport Landing.
A thousand river miles wound bobbinlike
away from weathered wharves and steamboat
bends
westward to the Missouri and the Kaw.
Poling in streams as muddy as catarrh
he cheered them singing *On our Kansas Claim,*
called it *Canaan of this latter day*
where free men bore their witness to the Truth.

At Westport, he laid in their provisions,
bartered for a wagon and a span of mules,
then cut his way cross-country to the Cygnes.
At water's edge, the grass grew horse-high rank;

on hills, waist-high to a man.
Prairie chickens gathered into autumn flocks
acres across, wild hops
raised canopies that covered walnut groves,
and bees shuttled in flyways through the dells.
Five miles west of Sugar Mound, he laid his claim.

Montgomery was a man who always seemed
to have a word working in his jaws:
here, his first was *thankfulness*; his second, *work.*
Through fall, he dressed and chinked their cabin
dry.
Clarinda and the boys bloomed around the hearth
where beans and coffee boiled and workshoes
warmed.
He let his beard grow black and ragged, but
as every neighbor came to know, his shirts
were starched as if for school.
Sundays at Sugar Mound he led their prayers
reading in a deep and evenhanded voice
the King James Jeremiad of Free Soil.

By fall of 1856, Missourians
made their play. Suddenly the name of *Clarke's*

. . . where free men bore their witness to the truth

Raiders cracked across the plains like dry
lightning, and Kansas rocked
limestone-deep in the thunder of their hooves.
At Linnville, they forced
seven fevered Free State men to drink
and empty every bottle in their cabins,
beat them senseless with their rifle butts,
and raped their wives. Then they swarmed to
Sugar Mound.
At gunpoint, they made Montgomery watch
his cabin burn, and jeered
The safest place for Abolitionists is North.

In morning light the Raiders' hoofprints showed
out southward black as bullwhip stripes, each
testament to slavery's ultimate reason.
Montgomery for the first time felt that stir
of righteous wrath that burns away the shell
of reticence and makes men act. Violence
would answer violence,
clandestine and quick. That night, sixteen men
gathered where Montgomery's house had stood.
Ankle-deep in ashes, they joined hands and swore
to bring in other Free State families,
then pledged their lives and fortunes to each
other—

that three rifle shots would bring them armed
to ride under Montgomery, night or day.

Since posses of slaveowning men patrolled
the Fort Scott road, the Brotherhood rode
deep in timber to a meeting place.
There, James Montgomery laid out plans to build
a kind of house *more suited to our needs*
and climate. Daily, armed parties went
down to the water, cutting oak and walnut.
Eight-foot logs were hewed, a center section
contoured out in each, and tenons cut
at either end. Each log was numbered, then
covered with brush. Next Montgomery chose his
site
high on a hillside. There they laid a stone
foundation topped by logs mortised to fit
the numbered tenons. On March the twelfth,
at dawn, his men assembled all the timbers,
stood them up on end, bored
augur holes, and drove mortise and tenons tight
with oaken pins. Mortised logs received the top
tenons, and puncheon doors were hinged. In a day
of quick and clever work, Fort Montgomery rose
strong as Solomon's temple on its hill.

Above log scallops and rifle ports
walnut rafters carried a roof of shakes
rived out of oak: from it, he perceived
the land at last was his.
Justice was next. Montgomery took the guise
of travelling Master, rode
into Missouri, and when he found that Clarke
had not returned he took a school and nights
neighbored from hearth to hearth, working out
the Raiders' names. Two weeks hence he rode
hard home,
raised his company, and led
them into secret camp. Two of his men
he dressed as Indians: his enemies supposed
Miami bands nearby and sent out word
to Clarke. His men came singly or in pairs
only to make rendezvous with Kansas men
who jumped them, took their money, guns, and
mounts,
and brought reparations back to Sugar Mound.

And settlers said, *One month with Montgomery*
gave us back our claims and dignity.

For that year and the next, there was peace.
Governor Geary chose to ignore the claims
and counterclaims, said they were merely sparks
out of the statehood bellows
but sent a man he called a Marshal down
to Sugar Mound, warning them against
lawless reprisals. Montgomery threw him out.
Slowly, he had come to see that those
who wanted Kansas slave were Whig as well
as Democrat: they knew no politics
but strength. Then a territorial court
was called in Bourbon County, and juries named
to scrutinize the claims along the Cygnes.
Beneath a Fort Scott poplar tree, that court
rescinded Free State claims in summonses
scrawled *B. Whacker.* A year of armed defense
had cost Montgomery his crop; he found
his family larderless in winter,
and now, ordered off their land. He called
his men to take the step that destiny
made absolute: summoning themselves,
they formed a Free State County Court, confirmed
their right to titles, claims, and deeds,
and then addressed the Territory:
Truth cannot be bought, burned, or terrorized:
Kansas will be free—we are the living proof.
Send your Marshal—better, send us Clarke.

Adversity had made Montgomery hard.
Inside his fort, Clarinda found her life
was pinioned to the fire—food for sixteen men
on Mondays; Tuesdays, husband gone and cows
staked in the pasture, waiting to be milked;
Wednesdays, walking down the hillside, knowing
  where
a hummock-hidden ambush lay;
Thursdays, waiting for her husband trapped
in tall grass without, and calling in
the cows and dropping there the food she hid
under her skirts; Friday nights, when he at last
lay sleeping on the pallet, her hand
clasped in his own, how a sniper's bullet
smashed against a rafter
and fell like a penny on her pillow.
That spring, one of the mules grew breachy,
leaned down a fence, and went across the field
to eat green corn. Johnny was sent to bring
him back. The neighbor saw him with the mule
and slapped his face. James came riding in,
saw, and started with his gun to settle
in his rage. She threw her arms around him,
pulling him from his horse, pleading not
to do the thing he ever would regret.

Only when the horse had dragged her ankles
raw in thistles did he care to stop
and turn, silent and withdrawn, for home.
He never went again, but mornings stepped
to a scallop in the wall, sighted down
four hundred feet along the valleyside
and knocked a cloud of rockdust in the air.
He rode more often, nights; when he returned,
he rarely gave his reason or his where.

In 1858, Lecompton's fraud
of Territorial elections made
Montgomery order daily drill. They called
themselves *militia,* and gave both bed and horse
to Old John Brown of Osawotamie,
long-sufferer of cause, who knew as well
as anyone the murderous intent
of slavers: knew that a vicar of the Lord
could shoot an unarmed Free State man and smile
to Bushwhacker applause. *Better a whole
generation die in violence, man,
woman, and child, than uncross a* t
in Free State, he proclaimed. In March, a band
of Raiders struck at Denton's, cutting the old
man down with buckshot in his cabin door.
His wife replied by throwing dippersful

of boiling water in their faces,
and one named Fort Scott Brockett shot her too.
The saber and the rifle, muttered Brown.
Montgomery agreed. A few dissented,
saying they believed the courts would someday
prove the Free State cause—but when Dred Scott
uncrossed another *t,* it was they who came
to call for Brown as Adjutant—came to love
the old man on his chestnut, in velvet-blue
slouch hat, crimson cape, and flowing foot-long
  beard;
and Montgomery, hard erect, in black, his bay
as lithe as steel—called them both *hardriders,*
the Saul and Jonathan of latter day.

III

THE MEETING AT JACKSON'S STORE

THE MEETING AT JACKSON'S STORE

Bates County, Missouri
May 18, 1858

They come from Syracuse and Terre Haute.
Riding West, they leave cracker boxes and glass
about, but when they go back East, all
they leave is rabbit hair and fieldlark feathers.
You all have seen them when they lay blue-lipped
and torpid in the cold, twenty below;
that spring, so weak they couldn't stand, they
crawled
to eat the grass and berries on their hands
and knees, vomit and eat, until their legs
would hold them up. That is what I mean.
What do they sow? Their oats, their corn, their
millet,
to burn and blast in southwest winds. They don't
care.
They seek no home or comfort on our land.
The hills are sacrifice, and rivers, creed.

And Denton was the worst. Hardhanded, wet
with sweat, he drove his mules like horses, drove

his land as if it owed him debt, and called
the cold of '55 and three months dry
of summer '57
recompense for wicked, blackheeled slaving men.
Hamelton, maybe you
could take as much, but when I go for mail,
and Denton stands there, guns my way, and says
Send your letters down through hell, *I'll gun him*
back.

I say Kansas is not for such as him:
we stand like on a shore where big-boled trees
enfold the waterholes and lines of brush
hold up the sky, but on beyond, the surf
is shorteyed grass and spikey cactus, hills
give way to mounds and hummocks, and the
brown
buffalo spill like shadows of a thundercloud.
Last December, we contrived to hunt
those herds that straggled down to Walnut Creek:
even James Montgomery came,
Colpetzer, Snyder and the rest, to shoot
a winterful of meat and blanket skins.

But after butchering and settling shares,
Denton and that hangdog missionary Read
rode away to Westport, on church affairs,
and you and I were countryboy enough
not to mind their reason.
They loaded in their crates marked bibles
and when they got them here
what they loaded out was rifles—Christian Sharps'
repeaters. Then I knew the jack was down:
Denton played the card, and there was only one
a man could play to it. It was a fight,
pick it now or later.
He knew as well as me it had to be.

We stood his cabin on the Little Osage,
Aaron Cordell behind the live oak,
Billy Griffith next the stovewood. I called,
Denton, there's a preaching going on
at West Point. Lend a Scripture we can take.
One of the new ones you just got. *Silence.*
Then I heard the slink
a rifle barrel makes taken off the wall.
The door swung out. I'll blow you through, *he said*
and stepped around the jamb. My shot spun him back

and down. Then I heard what sounded like
a rush of wings around my head, and boiling
water in my face.. Aaron said she threw it
dipperfuls. I fired my second barrel blind.

Brockett paused, and ran his hatbrim through his
hands.
Griffith, Hubbard, the Yealocks and Cordell,
Charles Hamelton, the one named Hardin Sheek,
leaned against the shelves, sat on their haunches
or on bags of beans. Jackson took his elbows
off the counter. *Free Staters is trade for me,*
he said. *That's the way I feel.* Brockett looked
around. *It was a fight and it was fair.*
I don't incline to worry where they bought
their beans. Hamelton laughed. *Listen now*
to Scotty talking—Brockett, it was you
declared your Grand Jury would jink the Free
Staters out by August last. And now it's May!
Out the windowpane, Brockett watched a cloud
humping along the slope of Spy Mound.
I said this latitude
was not for corn, but hemp; not for towns,
but gangs of Africans. Any fool can see.
Once we didn't rather more than misplace

a Free State mule to make them weary out.
But ones like Denton cut their teeth on granite.

The cloud had disappeared and now the scrub
stood silhouette against a shell of sky.
Hamelton propped his boot against the wall.
Brockett, you know the steam
sawmill they're building on the Cygnes?
You know the valley's bought
and platted? You know by who? A Senator,
Bigler, from Pennsylvania. You know what for?
The Great Missouri River-Fort Smith railroad.
He drove his heel against the boards, and flushed.
If Boston Henry Beecher
sends them rifles on a riverboat, let
them lay just half a mile of track and by
God Scott you'll see a cannon screwed aboard
the first train out of Westport aimed to blow
you and hemp and mules and niggers all to hell
and never let a living Southern soul
set foot that side of County Bates again.

Hamelton stood up. He leaned against
the window, his beard gold as a god's

in sun that runs the vault of heaven. *And that*
is just the half: the other half is this—
once we had a choice: if Eli Snyder
went to Trading Post
to cast a vote to dispossess a man
of land and servants, we could cast a score
and go that night to flavor up his well
with spurge. Today, they're voting on the third
constitution in as many years.
They've run us out. They've run you Yealocks
out;
they've run out Scott; and my claim has a stake
they've pounded in the well-curb where their
trains
will ditch piss-water. Eli Snyder won't
be waiting long to write his Massachusetts
moneylenders for the cost our claims
will run in taxes, and when he does,
by God we won't have any dollar auctions.
Hardin Sheek looked up. His beard was grown
around
a scar from mouth to collarbone. *We seen*
the sword, that it was buried in our flesh,
he said. *We seen firebrands James Montgomery*
loosed
to burn Jim Wells's store at Willow Springs.
We heard his words: Let vengeance fall upon
both the guilty and the indifferent.

I've rode with Clarke. And now I want to say,
someday soon we have to settle up,
you and me and everybody here.

A flight of crows tumbled out of the trees
like pepper. When they had passed, Griffith spoke
quietly, and dealt his words like cards.
Montgomery's made a list. He keeps one sheet,
Brown has one, Eli Snyder has the third.
When Will Allen drilled with them, he saw
the names: mine is there, yours, Fort Scott's,
Cordell's,
all of us. It says: These were the Haleys
of trafficked flesh in Kansas. Now there is not
room sufficient to accommodate
both them and us. We are the majority:
we decree these men should gather traps,
and should they then return, they forfeit
both their chattels and their lives.
He says they even put a bounty
on us. Hamelton's breath caught sharp. He
turned,
as Griffith finished. *They put a what?*
A bounty, Griffith said. Hamelton went
white: *Turned out and dispossessed, and now*
to put a foot across a Federal line

they say they'll hunt us down. Let your oxen out
to tall grass pasture near that line, or go
for deer or buffalo, they'll hunt you down;
they'll hide in broken country with their Sharps
and let you walk two hundred yards inside
before their first shot drives you hard for cover—
the next shot before you, then one behind—
then they run you round in circles, till you stand
winded, your eyes half blind with alkali,
while Eli Snyder sets his sights along
your buttons . . . shot like a scrawny, spring coyote,
and then they kick you over, bellyup,
cut off your tail and hang it on their fence . . .

I say God damn it no! they won't do that
to me or you. He wheeled around, excited,
almost hoarse: *Listen, tomorrow sunup*
I'm going to make an expedition south
along the Cygnes. If you men want to come,
then I say come. But I want no man here
at daybreak who is not hardriding. One
thing more: no man goes who'll not obey
my orders. I mean exactly that. I mean
those Free State bastards need attending to.
Hamelton turned and strode out through the
door.

The others watched him mount and ride off east;
they stood, and did not move or speak until
his horse was out of sight. Then the Yealocks left,
saying, *We'll be here tomorrow.* Griffith left,
Cordell. Hubbard rose and looked around:
There's whiskey on the counter, Jackson said,
while Brockett walked outside. Sheek untethered
for him: *You'll be here*? Brockett nodded. *Kansas
is festered proud with Free State men,* said Sheek,
*and we should put the lance to cautery
and dig out the root. Snyder, I mean.*
Brockett said, *There's a deal to hate in him.*
Then he mounted, and turned his horse toward
West Point.
An angry man won't watch the ground, he
thought.
His eyes are all ahead. Everything is there,
what he hunts, its tracks and shadow. But he
himself leaves tracks, casts a shadow. His hand,
moving triggerward, is only one of two.

IV

MIRIAM NICKELL'S LETTER TO HER MOTHER

MIRIAM NICKELL'S LETTER TO HER MOTHER

Willie was restless in his crib. I sat
next the window with my sewing—those days
that Samuel served as judge in Free State Court
I set aside for fancy work. The sun
spilled warm across my hands, and I had just
begun to work a twist of scarlet silk
into the outlines of a rose, when two
shadows on the road appeared; then two, and two
until at last a score of riders reined
around Spy Mound. I thought *more buffalo?*
but they are prime in winter. Then I saw
the two on foot, their hands behind: a man
named Wing, who ran a sawmill on the Cygnes,
and Johnny Campbell, his shirt bloody and torn.

I can't express the depths of fear I felt,
nor how the column, slowing, palled in dust,
held me helpless. We had lived through Clarke,
watched him burn our house, watched his raiders
  cut
off our chickens' legs
and write *Abol* across the coop in blood.

But this was daylight:
Charles Hamelton rode first, and their gait
was not of raiders or of fugitives,
but of an army come to strike us down.

I couldn't move. I thought how just five months
before, all of us had gone to Walnut
Creek, how Hamelton and James Montgomery's
men
had organized the buffalo brigades, named
common constables and sworn the rules,
how they'd run the chase, turned the bulls and
cows
suddenly short and cut them down with fire,
and how we women worked in pairs to cut
the living hide from off
the backbones, strip them, then cut off handles
of flesh and run our knives a semicircle
round the humps, then the flanks, the ribs, the
necks.

Mother, we were far from our New England.
And we were hungry. You would have done

"Miriam, I want Sam," was all he said.

as we, and afterward, at creekside, the moon
rushing through sheep-flock clouds—with blazing
fires,
the smell of fresh-braised meat—
like us you would have talked and sung and storied
till the skies showed gray.
And just at dawn, with our meat packed in,
the oxen still shaking with the smell of blood,
I felt so strange—not sad or unhappy,
—exalted, yet foreboded, just as if
it had been a kind of feast
for whom, for what, we never surely knew.

But this was daylight, and now I saw
the horsemen at my door. Hamelton walked
in. *Miriam, I want Sam,* was all he said.
His words were clear, but I could see his hands—
the knuckles all were white. *Charles,* I said, *he's
gone.*
He drew his pistols. Two of his men
burst through the door, and one
called Aaron Cordell then said, *I'll look around.*
I hadn't moved. I slowly put my needle
in my apron, and looked at Hamelton.
You know his court's today, I said. But then
he spoke as I had never heard before,

cursing me to my face. *Another lie,*
he kept repeating, *damnèd Free State lie.*

He motioned, and his men began to search
the cabin. First they cast the bolsters down
and overturned the pallets. They seemed
to want to walk their boots on what was clean,
and all the curtainings that hid our clothes
came down, and then the clothes. Then my wild-
plum
jams were smashed across the floor. I made a move
to stop this man-style bullying; Hamelton
raised his guns and said, *Hold still.* They burst
the latches of our trunk and raised the top.
Cordell upturned it on the floor and kicked
our linens into the mess of glass and jam.
Mister Hamelton, I said, *I think*
you'd better tell your men that if they don't
restore my things and make immediate
amends, they'll have to reckon
with my husband. And his friends. His lip twitched
once.
His florid, strongjawed face was set so hard,
yet for a minute, I believe he was
afraid. But then he said, *Mrs. Nickell,*
our reckoning is now. Once and for all.

With that he turned to one whose nose was hung
among his features like a bell-clapper,
whose eyes had unashamedly been fixed
on me these minutes past,
and said, *Matlock fetch a ladder and look*
what's hidden in the loft.
Matlock thrust a finger in his nose
and looked around. *Sam's not there,* I said,
but if it will content you, there's a ladder
out behind. Matlock shuffled out of doors.
Suddenly, our clock
began to chime. Hamelton and Cordell
both whirled around, and then they saw it perched
along the loft-ledge. Nine times it struck,
and Willie cooed for all it pleasured him.
Brought it all the way from Massachusetts?
Hamelton asked. *Yes,* I answered, and then
I don't know why I said it, but it came:

For all your malice and abuse, we like
to run our lives as punctual as trains.
At that, they gave each other such a look—

half of surprise, half of a kind of red
and angry intuition. Hamelton said,
I reckon that's the truth.
But all the while his anger mounted up.
You could see his lips were moving, *yes,*
they said, *she's right.* He grimaced, then fell
silent.
I wondered what had put him off that way.
He was a man disposed to take offense,
but he was not unkind; and hitherto
had never closed himself behind his blinds
to snipe at passersby, like others had.
But I was not aware of what he thought.
I was alone, with Willie, and now, afraid.
Matlock brought the ladder in and stood
it to the loft. *Drag the old boy down*
by his britches, said Cordell, and laughed.
Matlock started up. *If you knew us well,*
I said, *you'd know that Sam would never hide.*
Cordell screwed up the corners of his mouth
and switched his chew. *All of them hide,* he said,
one time or another. I've pulled your Pat
Devlin from a loft, and twenty more besides.
Boots first or shirt tails out, when they come
they come like ready apples off a tree.
And all we have to do is shake the branch
a little bit, just a little bit.

What he intended was to frighten me;
instead, with Matlock rustling up above
amongst our venison and bags of beans,
nice dried apples, patches, and crinkly canes
of raspberries we used for tea, I thought
You might have dragged your colored runaways
to light that way, but not a freeborn man.
The thought restored my calm, and so I stood
as Matlock called, above, *Captain Hamelton*
there ain't nobody here, but there's a side
of venison looks pretty good to me.
Hamelton put his pistols down. *All right,*
he said; and then I thought, *Thank God, they'll*
  now
content themselves to steal.
We heard Matlock begin to slide the meat
along the rafters; then his boot appeared
along the ledge. He was on his belly,
the meat clutched underneath him: he reached
his boot to find the ladder. I recall
Hamelton moved his head impatiently
as Matlock toed the air, trying to find
the rung. Suddenly, Matlock put his boot
against the clock and pushed, then pushed again,
and lazily it spilled over the ledge

and hung a moment, ticking; had I thought
of where it stood I would have thrown myself
beneath it. But I was still returning thanks
that they would only steal. And so it fell.
It whirred and cracked, and then the chimes
    began
to clash, crashing over the crib in which
my Willie lay. There was a silence,
deathly still. I couldn't speak. I only saw
his little hand was flexing, underneath.

I ran and ripped the heavy clockworks off,
the chimes and walnut case, the splintered rails.
His head was gashed, his eyes were open,
and they were turned up white. I held him tight
against me, stanching up the flow of blood
in fancy work. *Murderers,* I said, and then
again, *murderers,* and then I shouted
murderers, rocking my Willie, *murderers.*
I screamed as loud as they could hear, and then
again. Cordell suddenly leaped across
the room and put his gun against my head
saying, *Howl, damn you, howl!* and so I screamed
again. Hamelton lunged and took the gun
away from my temple, and I stopped.
Matlock, get down, he said. I heard the man

descend and walk outside. *Let's get on,*
Cordell, said Hamelton, *there's nothing here.*
She'll raise all hell, Cordell broke in. *I think . . .*
and then I didn't hear the rest, for Willie's
head was swollen so around the gash;
I dropped the cloth in water and pressed
it up against the swelling, kissing his cheeks
and eyelids. After a while, they left. Willie
cried and cried as I dressed his wound. I looked
outside. The dust was settling, and they were
  gone.
Later, as Willie slept, I sat down again.
The sun was blinding hot, and I thought of O!
the water, gushing in stony streams of our
New England, how I parched for it, and I cried . . .

V

STATEMENT BY THE REVEREND MR. B. L. READ

STATEMENT BY THE REVEREND MR. B. L. READ

Seek, and ye shall find. Seek, as we have found.
We reap an amber plenitude beside
the honey-humming dells—Marais des Cygnes, that
 flows
broad-shouldered in her banks,
breaking in shoals
and rapids near the mounds crested with rock—
hickory, walnut, hazel and pecan—
plum, persimmon—throngs of antelope and deer—
Empire in anarchy, waiting for hands
to shape it into barn and hayrick!
That May nineteenth, I was watching just
such hands as Pat Ross harnessed up a horse
for marking out a stand of corn. A smart
southwester tossed the poplar leaves on top
of Timbered Mound as Ross sank in the share.

We talked about a school, for raising two
years hence, and Pat then pointed out a stand
that we might log for siding and the floors.
It put to mind an Indian convert, old
and resolute, who watched
us cleave first furrow up on Mission ground.

He knelt and thrust his hand
knuckle-deep in loam, fingering it. Then
he stood and looked at us. *Wrong side up*
was all he said, before he walked away.

That tickled Pat. He laughed, throwing the reins
around his shoulders, leaning back to halt
and more enjoy it. *Featherheaded buck,*
I never saw! We laughed, and as we did
the timber near the water seemed to rise
at us with echoes. His horse whickered once
as if amused, and as we paused for breath
to laugh again, there was another—not
from the water, but behind.
And then I felt a touch of cool along
my back. It wasn't wind.
I turned and saw
Hamelton topping the pass on Timbered Mound.

He heeled his sixteen hands of stallion down
the trail, followed by what looked to be a score
of riders, and three on foot. *Read*! he cried,
reining, drawing off his gauntlet gloves.

Reverty, now this I count
a happy accident. Who's your friend?
A Christian, I replied.
Hamelton smiled. He drew and cocked his Colt.
The others had surrounded us. I saw
Johnny Campbell, Andrews, and Wing, on foot
behind. *Brockett*! Hamelton called. The one
who ran the Southern Hotel
pulled his handsome bay around and looked at us.

Denton's killer, whispered Pat, and then he spit.
Brockett looked at us with eyes that seemed
to limn some thought. *Bible-runners both,* he said.
Hamelton ordered us to fall in line.
He trimmed his aim: *You won't, will you*? I said
we willingly would do anything right.
Where we're going, we'll need
a minister, he said. One of his men
whose neck was split with scar got down to free
Pat's horse and another, working on a chew,
said, *That's a damned good horse there Sheek. I'd*
take
me a piece of that. Pat started for him,
shouting, *Thieving Bushwhackers*! but Brockett
interposed his bay. *Stay,* he said; Pat stayed.

Then William Stillwell happened atop the pass:
he braked his wagon, trying to turn, but soon
they brought him down. Young he was, and
  dressed
in Quaker gray. *Where the hell do you live?*
one demanded. *Friend, at Sugar Mound*
he said. *He looks like one of Jimmy's men*
another said, so Stillwell was put in line.
One of the Raiders called for riding on
to Fort Montgomery. *No,* said Hamelton.
Bring up those older ones. Andrews and Wing
came up, looked at us, then him. *I reckon you
would rather walk this wagon back than go
with us. We've got younger scalps to fry.*
They got aboard as Sheek unhitched the team.
That left Johnny Campbell and the three of us.
We marched along a wash
and crossed a stream. Some of the Raiders said
they hadn't ought to let the old men go
but Hamelton cut them off: *We had enough
doggery back at Nickells. Besides,* he said,
we've got railroad men and turncoats up ahead.

I cried: *Hamelton, the Lord hath said—*
thee I make a terror to thyself and all
thy friends. He didn't seem to hear, but held
his florid, handsome head
erect. What parasite sucked at his thought?
The slavery laws? That cause
was lost. Stealing horses? Montgomery's men?
If they were evening up, why not attack
the fort at Sugar Mound? . . . I could not fathom
them,
nor was I afraid: their desperation showed
no doctrine. It was clear
that we had cut the colter out of slavery
once for all in Kansas. It gave me great
confidence to sense that truth, feeling the firm
Semitic muscle in our Master's tongue
that made him prophesy *For I have come*
not to bring you peace, but a sword. We had
carved
with steel the Free State Kingdom of His Will.

We headed East, only a mile from where
Missouri lay in wait. The sun rode high
and hot and seemed to draw our blood around
its element. Grasshoppers leaped against

the horses' flanks. *Friend,* Stillwell whispered,
there's
a hundred dollars in
my boot. Don't favor it, I said; *they'll not*
perceive. He shook his head, *To think my wife*
had warned me. Young Campbell came up beside;
his shirt was bloodied. *They didn't get the Sharps'*
he whispered, *just some robes. Sufficient then*
unto this day the evil, I replied.
At Hall's they took old Amos from his bed
in fever, stood him in line, and Stillwell caught
his arm. We walked on East, slower, they
more wary as we cut across the grass
apron that fell from Hay Rick Mound. Ahead
lay William Colpetzer's claim. We could hear
his wife haranguing him to hide. *Domn*!
I vill not run! the Dutchman roared, so he
was also taken. We struck off North.
The vord is out, Colpetzer shook his fist,
and Copting Hommelton vill soon be dotching
shot!
Hamelton laughed. *You mean Montgomery's*
men?
They're gone. There's not an Abolitionist
for leagues; they're up at Sugar Mound. So let
your Jim Montgomery sleep, craving his fame,
without the guts a coyote has to get it.
I wouldn't waste the shot on such as him.

There was a bluish serpentine of smoke
rose from a cabin in a walnut copse
with piled-stone walls before and either side.
One of the Raiders spoke to Hamelton.
Go get him, Griffith, Hamelton said.
The other, small, with hob-heeled Texas boots,
took a pair of men along. They dropped behind
the wall as Griffith walked without a show
of hesitation in the door. For one
moment we only heard the wind skimmer
the bunch grass, waiting for the shout or shot.
Suddenly, two men walked outside, their hands
above, still in plowing clothes. No one knew them.
That was quick, said Hamelton.
You're Hamelton? said one, angry. Hamelton
nodded. Damn it, we don't even know
Montgomery. This man here's a guest of mine
from Illinois. Hamelton asked his name.
Charles Snider, the other said. *Illinois!*
roared Hamelton. *Damn Illinois! You're kin*
to Dutch Eli up at Priestly Mound
and he's our game, by God he is! Hubbard,
go and get their arms . . . And so we started off
again. *Dutch Eli?* said the one, *who's*
that? The other shook his head. *Oh God,*

he said, *how was I to know that he*
was looking for that name. And then the thought
struck out at me: *Hamelton has a list.*
He's not just raising hell, he has a list.
And there are other names than ours. And what
would be the end? And then I closed my eyes
a moment, breathing in; perhaps Hamelton
heard whispers from a Self we hadn't seen.

Amos Hall commenced to ask for drink.
Hamelton, I said, *you could at least*
give of a draught. Brockett pulled a flask
out of his dickey bag. He threw it down
to Hall and said, *The rest of you can wait:*
get it in hell with Reverty. Then Sheek
whispered to Hamelton; the Captain's face
mottled with excitement. We began to walk,
not aimless or tentative, but now
as if a groove guided our steps. The next
we took were William Hairgrove and his boy.
Join the Brotherhood, said Hamelton.
Hairgrove looked him over: *Why?*
I know the way you vote, Hamelton said.
Hairgrove kicked the dirt. *The hell you do.*
I'll show you how, said Hamelton, *you wait*
and soon by God you'll see . . . A kind of stiff

precision took a hold of him . . . *You'll see,*
he kept repeating. *My boy ain't part of it,*
said Hairgrove; *leave him out.* Hamelton cropped
his horse and hissed, *Nits grow into lice.*
Brockett tried to intervene, but Hamelton
cut him off. *The spawn goes with the stud,* he said,
and next is Snyder. They fell in line with us,
silent, and we walked toward Priestly Mound.

Soon
we heard the squeal of cart wheels, and a yoke
of oxen hove over the slope. Austin Hall,
half-blind with erysipelas, downed
the mound and dropped into the waiting web.

VI

THE MARRIAGE OF LILY STILLWELL

THE MARRIAGE OF LILY STILLWELL

Her kitchen is a moundslope, sinking down
to sycamores on Sugar Creek; behind
and either side rise prairie mounds as bald
and smooth as muffins in a tin. She stoops
before an open fire, trying to shield
it with her bonnet. The southwest wind blows
hard
enough to lean against, and throws up
piffles of dust against the covered pan
she used to raise salt yeast. She has laid
a line of chips behind the oven, and built
up stones around to keep chips, coals and pan
from blowing off. The flames rear up. She casts
her bonnet down impatiently and squats,
her skirts ballooning, trying to damp the fire.

Never a cloud today, never a mercy
from the sun. Her kitchen-fancy teases: vague
imaginings of drawers, the sharp report
a stoveslot makes, the reaching out to grasp
a cool and sweating handle
of a pump. *What Canaan land is this*? she asks
herself, feeling within

a surge of dark dimensions, then its ebb.
She banks the coals and glances at their ox,
horned, half-wild, tethered with a hawser.

And thinks, *The Territorial Road was best.*
William, thee'd not abide my words but said
to save a league cross-country valued more
than any Kansas Marshal's ridealong,
and when thee set thy mind, nothing availed.
Peace and probity are principles
nor Friend nor Christian denies, but where is
peace
if probity must mean to gainsay me
a certainty of mind
by riding off to Westport all alone?
She turns and looks inside the water jug,
then hefts it on her hip and pours a cup.

Silence. It is a skirring, slinking kind
of silence. At night, beneath the lean-to,
she hears a sound she thinks is made by stars
wheeling all bright and brittle overhead.
And just two months, she thinks.

Two months since stepping down the scrollwork
  iron
platform from the car
at Westport Landing. And William, still
in plaindress gray. *Dear heart, my own delight.*
He was thinner, and there was something brown
and hard about him pitching her stagecoach trunk
behind the buckboard. Then
he swung her up the step and sat her down.

And they were married in a kitchen.
No Philadelphia Meetinghouse, he joked
but whose are truer vows than ours? He hired
a minister named Read, and bade two Friends
named James and Lucy Marshall presence too
and they had spread the sink and stovetop thick
with flowers. How her head
had turned with smells that day at Trading Post;
of honeysuckle, sweet verbena, wild rose,
saddle leather, whiskey. With the tramp of boots
and chinking rowels and faces long removed
from soap and barbers, it was Babylon.
But in the moment of her vow, she felt
a kind of Lightslide of the Truth, within.

And then they brought the fiddlers, harp, and jug
and planktop tables. She had barely got
the pound cake cut when Read removed himself,
whispering to William. Others went out,
and only then she saw their guns. She sensed
how closemouthed William had become: she had
to ask, and ask again, till he at last
confessed he ought to ride to Sugar Mound.
And then she had to plead that he would not,
and he looked black, obviously torn. So then
they compromised and both drove off, leaving
the trunk, the flowers, the women, and the cake.
At Fort Montgomery, they passed guerrilla
columns off to raid Fort Scott. A piece beyond,
the slave named Winnie Campbell sat inside
a sod-roofed smokehouse,
suckling her child. Lily could see how used
she was to portering her loads atop
her head: even in grief, her backbone held
her face erect and proud. A blacksnake stripe
cut across her shoulder, fresh-swelling and pink . . .

. . . Lily drinks her water, thinking *How it looked*
easy in her dignity to bear that load
yet knows it is the bite of whip and wheel
of suffering's own momentum
that sustain the slave: so caught within
the press, he yields and stocks
his own arms taut for breaking. *Easy, yes*
she thinks *but only looked to be. Inside,*
a slave knows nothing but his death. That day
at Sugar Mound, she and William heard
how it began, to South
along the Red in Arkansas; how two
converts to William Garrison gave
Winnie all the rights they could, setting her
"free";
how Winnie married with a slave, Lewis,
and bore their child. But then the law required
Master-guardians for Freedmen—to comply
meant chatteldom, to refuse, the auction block.

Winnie began to hear about a trail
that led beyond Fort Smith, beyond Fort Scott,
out to an open prairie kind of place.
It was for twilight telling, what she heard,
ankle-deep in dust at cabin doors
when fires were lizard eyes:

exodus tales about a freedom road.
Lewis encouraged her to take the chance
and he would follow. She strapped the baby flat
against her back, with corn meal and chitterlings,
shallots and pecans and grapes and plums.
The trail unwound a half a thousand miles
across the mountains of the Ouachita.
She was tracked by slaving Indians in bands
whose sentinels she learned to read in dust;
hewed shelter from the chinkapin, hearing
the pish and whing of arrows in her wake.
Then it was white men in their bands who looked
for runaways; and descending from the blue
Ozark hills to a gulfstream surf of grass
that sighed and broke in continental winds
she ran with shrill piping of ball and buckshot
close at hand. But now at doors that opened
into food she heard of Free State Kansas,
and ninety days from Arkansas she crawled
up to Fort Montgomery's palisades
from Sugar Creek and saw its puncheons open.
Montgomery led her in and said *Woman,*
I pledge my word this fort will keep you free.

And James Montgomery's word held true. That
year

she lived in peace, but waiting, always waiting.
Buffalo came and went, the soldiers drilled.
Clarinda gave her washing and the water
walk. And then one night in June the woods
loosed a man dragging an iron shackle—
it was Lewis, wounded by shot, but safe.
Eli Snyder came to strike him free of chains
and set him up to farm, but in the fall
the Territorial Marshal left Fort Scott
and late one night his posse rode in hard
and ringed their place. *Lewis Campbell,* he called.
Surrender to the United States. And then
they stormed the smokehouse
dragging Lewis out and tying him astride
a mule. A man whose neck was split with scar
called for *taking in the wench* and riding
on to Fort Montgomery, but the Marshal told
him short. *The warrant reads that he's the slave*
he said. *She's free; so is the whelp.* And then
the man sawed on his reins and dug his spurs
crying *She's chattel too by God* and cut
her with his whip. And then they left, and when
the morning came, Lewis was back in chains . . .
. . . The fire that Lily tends is steady now.
The sun reels in a white and depthless sky.
She puts her bonnet on, then walks and sits
under the lean-to, in the shade. *And so*
for that one African they rode, she thinks

remembering how she had to plead again
with William not to ride: *To what thee does*
tomorrow I can not object, but this
is wedding day for me, breaking into tears . . .

Remembering how he turned the wagon back;
and she, watching the sun descending proud
and angry as a fireball in the banks
of clouds, hesitant to hold his arm,
still silent in the cricket-chorusings;
and then the drum of hoofbeats in the dusk,
how William cut the wagon from the road
dropping into the brush and pulling her
beside, and drawing from the box beneath
the seat a rifle, sighting now along
the road as horse and rider cantered like
some rusty pendulum in range, and then
her half-cry as William challenged *Stop*
or I shoot thee, the rider lying low
and spurring. Then he fired: three times he shot,
shot with a carnal instrument, to kill.
And how she thanked Providence that the balls
went wide, thanked with tears that meant both
shame
and something else—she might have called it joy,
or maybe terror. But never love.

Next day, she heard James Marshall was the man,
coming to ride them home from Sugar Mound . . .
. . . Lily lays her head across her arm.
William, thee is not for violence she thinks
yet feels a numbness in her limbs. A sense
of strangeness presses in around her like
the dry insistent beating of a locust's
wings. The wind rises and the longhorn ox
bellows, hoarse as a rifle volley.

VII

THE BATTLE AT SNYDER'S FORGE

THE BATTLE AT SNYDER'S FORGE

They ride in Legion now, six sixes deep,
legging like a spider up the slope
of Priestly Mound. Behind, along a white
limestone collarbone of creek, the brown
span of oxen cut from Austin Hall
graze haunch by jowl in greenstream grass.
  Hamelton
drives the phalanx needle north and up
to timber, where they rein along a line
of stumps below the chine. The Captain lays
a leg across his pommel, watching smoke
thumb up from somewhere on the other side.
Then he pulls his two-edged border knife, taps
the star-shaped rowel on his boot, and signs
for Brockett, Sheek, and Griffith to dismount.

The blacksmith draws his bellows like a pair
of shears, snicking the air in wedges
which he feeds in rapid fire through a hood.
Their rasps commence to anger up his mound
of charcoal to a white
ordeal for iron. He takes a candent bar,
throws it against the anvil,

beats until a crescent waxes red,
then dunks it in a puncheon brim to brimful
foaming with white artesian watersprings.

Behind a fan of tamarack, they lay
their eyeshot on the roof of Snyder's forge:
half a moundslide down, it turns
its face beyond, southwest along a snake
ravine that headlongs from the door, through elm,
poplar, a lone red haw, down to the green
meanders of the Cygnes. Behind and sides
the walls are limestone-blank. Griffith sets
his pantslegs down to hide
his boots. With gun and knife behind, he drops,
circles the shop. Brockett and Sheek remain.
Hamelton trails him down, his shotgun primed.

The squarejawed maul beats bell-like, and the
hand
and arm and crosspeen fall in cadence
to its calling. His arms and shoulders rise
out of a steerhide shield or apron like
a burst of copperheads
writhing around the black and hairy roots

of river sallows.
Eighteen leg-irons hang behind his forge.
Each clevis-pin is severed by the sharp
and burrless cut his hammer-arm has dealt,
each testifies to Truth rung deep in bone:
one arm, one steel, that sprung
a squad of squatheel slaves to life again.

Griffith stands before the shopdoor. He holds
both hands visible and still. In the dark
within, Snyder looms like a mesa, his maul
motionless, poised. The sun of two o'clock
is hot and slick, pinpointed in his eyes.
Be you Mr. Snyder? Griffith asks.
The maul descends once more
and sparks whorl up. *That's me* a voice replies.
There's a man out yonder wants to see you
Griffith says. The blacksmith lays his maul and
tongs
aside and turns to rinse his hands. *All right.*
And he will come: Griffith sees it, now.
It is as if the doorway were a chute;
he is the wrangler, Snyder is his meat.

He has anticipated this. Not the man,
the stranger standing with his gunhands poised;
but the call, the innocent request.
He too equivocates, nods his assent.
He lays his tongs athwart the charcoal while
he washes, takes them then, inconspicuous,
as if they were the watchfob to his hand:
blinks as his head emerges into sun,
engaging then the stranger's steady gaze,
saying, Where? *while slipping back his hand*
behind the cedar doorframe where a Sharps'
six-sided barrel meets the palm. He waits
a second as the stranger steps ahead
to lead him up, follows in the pinheeled tracks
a step behind. Up here *the stranger says*
just as they round the wall.
It is Hamelton, half a dozen yards
uphill. I've got you where I want you!
calls the Captain, his coatarms black with sweat.
Yes? You think you do *the blacksmith shouts*
and feels his right arm rising with the tongs.

The blacksmith towers like a timberline,
eyes and mouth inhumed behind his grizzled
beard. Hamelton feels his finger jump
against the dogstooth curve

of forward trigger, thinking, *There is such*
a goddamn lot of target
to him, to the limbs that seem to drop
like taproots from that trunk. Griffith yells
You dawn well know we've got you Eli—march!
and Hamelton calls *This way*! when then
the treetrunk splits as if
a bolt of lightning ran it through. For two
splitsecond seconds, Hamelton stands
hung on his tonguehold, and he sees a tongs
lash out and rip across Will Griffith's face,
hearing the scream of pain, seeing him then
begin to fall as Snyder's second limb
lashes the tongs again, and then again.

He turns to jump behind his wall and grab
the Sharps; feels himself turned again in turn
apron-to on Hamelton who fires a charge,
and feels the steerhide kick against his ribs,
the sting of buckshot laced with pepperpods
that sear beneath his skin.
Passing the corner now, the whing of shot
rides high and easy over. At the door,
he grabs the bluesteel barrel of the Sharps,
then drives the stud-iron door in place and bars
it shut. He legs across the room and stands

atop his bench, pulling a loosened stone
out of the topmost course. He sees the Raiders
still in range as Hamelton circles out
to run the door. Hoisting the Sharps, he feels
a ground glass bobbing back and forth within.
He sights along the Captain's pewter buttons,
fires. The rifle leaps and churns against him.
Damn! *he roars, half in pain, half for the gray*
flag of coattail that snaps and dives behind
a rock. He leans the Sharps against the wall
and loads. A pistol ball splatters across
the wall below. Now he can see a rifle
barrel glinting like a needle in the green
of tamarack along the ridge. He fires
again and roars Get up ye goddamned
blackheeled bastards *feeling his muscles close*
around the shot the way an oyster grows
around its stone until it smoothes to pearl.

There is a sow bug of a curse that squats
upon him now: Hamelton feels it suck
his hotsun blood, raging the while to shoot
the blacksmith through, to watch the plenum bile
spill out and dissipate, to crush the skull
and arch-coils of the Abolitionist.
He sights along the rockface at the hole

where Snyder's rifle winks: he fires again
and hears the rockchips spall in rattles.
He conjures: succeeds only in summoning up
the Snyder he has met six weeks before
crooking a Sharps across his arm. *That looks*
just like a rifle, Hamelton had said;
you'd better treat it careful
if you go on past Trading Post. At that,
the blacksmith turned his gaze, and he could see
the blackash eyes that onced him up and down.
If you know better Snyder said *then why*
even ask? Hamelton had felt a kind
of organ bellows pulsing in the air:
black, rebellious Northern blood, that would have
been
at Black Jack and Osawatomie.
The Captain thought to burn him then and there.
Keep the Sharps at home he said *or else*
I'll blow you through. The blacksmith raised his
gun
as smooth and quick as oil. *If you don't leave*
I'll take you off that horse.
He takes his Colt
and fires it at the window, yelling now
to Sheek and Brockett for a covering fire.
Resting his shotgun in the shade of rock
he sees a salamander shake its tail

and scrabble back and forth across a ledge,
back and forth, ruby-eyed and insolent.

The shots spat wide around his rifle port.
Fragments of ball and stone tear at the hide
he wears. Now he hears their words, rising like
black
expectant carrion birds: he moves his hand
as if to brush a dross of spiderweb
away, and smiles. It is foregone, *he thinks.*
Let Hamelton rage. Let him peel his hide.
He loads and fires. His Sharps can speak three
words
for every Southern syllable of shot.
Now they are firing from the hilltop, hot
for Hamelton's retreat. He pauses. Then
the Captain makes his dash, and Snyder shoots
again, almost reflectively, along
the row of buttons; sees him crack his stride
and fall loose-legged in a bush. Silence.
He loads, and hears a sound of voices near
the door. He knows that they will be a party
taking up the man. On the slope, Hamelton
rears, running out of range. He lays the Sharps
aside and slips down slowly from the bench,
leaning his arm beneath the waterflow

above the puncheon; lets the current pour
across his arm and shoulder, spinning the clot
to chips and coils and bloody filaments.
He sees his blood oiling the surface
of his tank, beneath the hanging irons:
it spills out of the puncheon now, spills
beneath the wall, spills into the long ravine,
down to the green meanders of the Cygnes.

VIII

THE MASSACRE

THE MASSACRE

Spraddle-legging through thistle and dry
dissilient milkweed pods. The bunch grass boiling
up beneath his boots in humps, splaying
like surf along a shore. Cursing himself,
the mumping rifle balls, the slickleaved shade
cover thrown by osage oranges in plats
along the slope. Cursing the curse, the black
boa coils of happenstance, and the man
unseen, erect behind the blank stone wall.
He dives beneath a bush, feeling a warm
purling of air behind a ball, and thrusts
his head and shoulders underneath a vine.
Crowfoot. It is a leafy, bitter smell,
rooting in blindworm runners down to dark.

A sawkneed cricket chirrs into his ear.
He thinks God damn. You goddamned fool.
Snyder
pinked you good. *The sun is slipping down its rim*
into the flange of hills. Twelve, he'd wanted.
Twelve for him to kangaroo.
You lost him. *A vial of leadheaviness*
spills into his blood.
He makes himself resist, biting the lining

of his mouth. Gonna write it on the wall,
he thinks; write it big, write it in blood.

The nib of powderhorn gouges his side,
the pouch of shot, the shotgun, dry and hot.
He feels a vapor tracking up his arm,
roiling the blood; now his shoulder, neck
start like a flickertail. It infiltrates
his body corridors, undoing hasps,
firing the puncheons of his brain. They fall
and all the feeding flames within shoot high,
whipped by the windmill arms
of prairie wind, swatching in sheets across
the sky, detonating groves of sycamores,
birling the horn-locked herds of buffalo.

And feels a thought he does not think: can feel
his head rise up, feels all himself plucked up,
the tendons of his legs snapping against
the bones, raising the shell of vines until
his arms and backbone burst
out of the overgrowth, and he is free.
He hears no shooting, now.

He runs along the slope, ramming a set
of charges home. Brockett! *His badger's face*
flinches in surprise. Get the goddamned horses!
Griffith's bad *the other says.* Dammit Scott
get yourself a move on!
bracing in the saddle and turning back.

And rides them down: the Abolitionists
hold their faces half a breath removed
from fear. Even his Raiders seem to wait,
unhoping what comes next. He can discern
the worm in all of them, looking across
to shade, where Griffith holds his tong-raked face.
Talk has never been
equivalent to commands. *The Captain looks*
at Luke and William Yealock, squat on mules
and blank as bassets; at Michael Hubbard,
robes and a bottle tied across his saddle.
Matlock balances boots, hung by a knot
athwart his shoulder. Brockett and Cordell
repose in shade, letting their horses graze.

Ready, Captain. *It is Sheek. In his bone*
and onyx eye, Hamelton perceives

something he knows. Something he has seen,
not yet, yet there. Knowing. He knows. As well
as he. By God we'll write it big, *he thinks,*
and calls: Fall in! *The faces stare as though*
they hadn't heard. Matlock! Brockett! Sheek!
Git to gitting! *sidling his stallion in*
amongst the Abolitionists, shouldering hard
until they give or sprawl. Belial! *the old*
missionary shouts. Moloch! *The stallion*
knees him down. Git! *And they form, and file*
slowly across the moundcrest toward a slope
fevered with sumac. Hamelton rides
around the column, shoves the straggling Halls,
kicks at the Yealock mules.
Only Sheek has seemed to comprehend
Hamelton's intent, riding herd in front.
He drives them up the slope to where a dark
declivity begins in yarrow. Now.
Hamelton spurs. It is as clear as glass.

It is the avenue. For them. For him.
He plunges in the mouth of the ravine,
trampling the brush. March in here! *he shouts.*
And they turn, with Sheek beside
tamping them through the orifice. Hamelton
turns to watch them coming in:

the first is Robertson, red enough
to boil. Snyder is next, Eli's kin,
and Read, swelling with belly rumbles.
Ross, the Irishman, smiles with half a mouth.
The Quaker walks behind,
staring stones to life, and limping. Amos Hall.
And rear, the pimply Hairgrove boy, who walks
eyes closed, father behind, looking back
and swearing now. The blinded Hall who holds
the Dutchman's arm. And last, the little clerk
and riflemonger Campbell, leading up
the rear, edging between the yarrow arms.

The Captain leads them down along a choked
descent that jaws them to a single file.
Here the sumac cools to cottonwoods,
the ground is smooth, grassy as a road.
Halt! *They stop.* Face right. *He smiles, feeling*
pleased.
You tell them pick, they pick.
Up along the walls, *he tells the Raiders*:
they ride on either side of the ravine
to pastern-high above the line of men.
We're going to see what Abolitionists
have got for guts, *the Captain says.* Montgomery,
Brown, and all your men will have to look

a month to find your pieces. Raise your arms!
he calls, reaching for his shotgun. Gentlemen,
he hears, if you intend to shoot, then take
good aim. *It is Hairgrove, drawling now,*
mocking his very tone of voice: he spits
neatly between the hooves of Hamelton's horse.
Fire! *is in his mouth to say, when he hears*
Brockett don't obey. *It is Sheek, who points*
along the line to where the bay and rider
stand. You raise your piece! *the Captain cries.*
I'll be God damned if I will! I'll fight,
but I won't butcher! *Brockett turns his horse.*
Then Luke and William Yealock back away.
You stay right there! *Hamelton cries.* By God
Scotty you've got a cow turd on your neck
instead of head! You lost your nerve? You don't
cotton to this? You want to take them home?

He rises in his stirrups, voice and arm
and fist flogging against the flow of air
along the grass ravine: Remember Scott
and all the rest of you, your names are down
on Jim Montgomery's list. Screw me now or not,
they are. And my first charge is primed to fire.
Heist your asses now and see: anyone
not in line and firing gets the second!

. . . as the line breaks, splitting and plunging

Brockett swings his horse around and pulls
his shotgun from its scabbard, Will Yealock
points a rifle, Luke a Colt. Present your arms!
Now they all are up. And the Captain sets
his sight to where the ramping sun has rolled:
by raising up his hand
he can contrive to turn the iron valves of sky
and tap the utter shales beyond, to flood
the vaults of heaven with diluvium,
to ride upon the baulks of earth, the winds
beating around these molehill mounds, and swamp
the fires of all of them, drown them all
with one thunderstone of Force, sinking the sun,
the mazing corridors of space: his arm
cocked like a Cheyenne bull-roarer against
the falling sky, hingeman to the helm
of history, joint to them all, the ruck
millenial since Cain, who watch from files
beyond the skyfolds he is flooding down.
Write it in blood. *And brings his right arm down,*
his Fire! *and roar of shotgun bounding back,*
doubled again on down the line, his aim
centered on Campbell's belly, as the line
breaks, splitting and plunging, with aftercry
and murmur of surprise and lasting sprawl . . .

He is off and standing now, feeling a warm
gloving on his fingers, of blood that spills
slow as honey from Campbell's side. A shout
pulls up his glance along the rise. Brockett turns
his horse and runs. The Yealocks follow suit.
Hubbard looks around; he sees but does not seem
to care. They're not all dead *the Captain says.*
Let's finish them. *Sheek bends down beside*
a body holding its dead belly like
it ached. There's old Read *says Sheek.* And which
is he? There's the old bastard looking up.
Put the pistol to his ear, *the Captain says,*
shoot him into his ear. Turn the Quaker's
pockets out, *says Hubbard;* I heard him say
a hundred dollars. Here's his watch and fob . . .
. . . A crow caws from a pocketfold of tree.
No one ever wrote it bigger. Abol,
melting along the bunchgrass floor in slick,
uncertain rubrics. Prairie spatterdock,
crimson, weeding down to limestone springs . . .
. . . A wind rises along the grass ravine.
The Quaker holds a green and yellow flower
burst from the house his bellymuscles built . . .
. . . He is alone. Sheek has ridden down
the mound. He is clean. He is clear. He lifts
his boot, then heels into the stirrup. Behind,
the track of hooves, his bootprint. He turns,
descending. His horse, the bodies, and their dark
vital lava, convolve in shadowfall.

IX

THE HANGING OF WILLIAM GRIFFITH

THE HANGING OF WILLIAM GRIFFITH

October 30, 1863

They came from Farlinville, Paris, La Cygne,
their wagons slow as landsnails, the wheels
squealing as they climbed a hump of bunchgrass
and then hammered down the dip. A troop of
horse
wound its way cross-country. Others walked
with bedrolls on their backs along the slope
of Sugar Mound. The day was windless, clear.
The prairie year was closing up its eye
on bluestem dunned to straw, on yarrow bolls,
on panicle and leaf of sumac afire
in clumps among the oaks at Barnes's store;
on beaver, blue, and brass of state militia
and spiderwork of frame and courthouse brick
rising from a foursquare green beyond

where William Hairgrove sat on a plank, his gray
eyes surmising who and why they came.
A block away, Will Griffith sat inside
his pineboard cell. *Not much longer,* Hairgrove
thought.
He stood, straightening his back,

and looked around the square—at Colpetzer's wife,
Amos Hall, and all
the ones he didn't know, or only thought
he knew; and some in uniform or bits
of Blue, and women now, more now than then

when Hamelton had sown his bloody oats
broadcast across the mounds at Trading Post . . .
. . . and all the ones not there to see: his son,
drafted to infantry; Montgomery, Colonel
to Colored Carolina Troops; Brown,
a martyr in Virginia; and the Five
faces, dearer for nubbing down in time
to likelessness, like stone, never to rise
to hand or voice again:
Johnny Campbell, Stillwell, Patrick Ross,
all shot and knifed; Colpetzer, wrathless now,
and Robertson, a man they never knew;

and Six still bound to life—the Hairgroves, Snider,
Read, all freighting shot, Amos Hall
who'd spat out ball and cartilage from where
they drilled his cheeks, and Austin Hall who heard
the skirr of death and fell

Hall's oxen pulled him past the crowds . . .

woundless, his eyes pussing like punctured boils,
and afterwards had felt
the warm worming of the air that slid along
the grasstops, and worse, over the pain,
had sensed his soul squeezing against the cold
bodystones fallen from their firmament
until some Providence
keyed them in their bleeding arch again . . .

. . . *Ready*. The Sheriff stood with axe and hood,
a wagonload of coffin just behind
and flanked beyond by ranks of blue militia.
Hairgrove rose into his saddle, and watched
the celldoor open as the prisoner emerged.
A squad closed in and sat him on the raw
coffinlid. Hall's oxen pulled
him past the crowds and wagons and the troops;
in turn, they followed, silent, as if the ox
unbound the stillness of the oaks, the great
maples sapped and red-heavy with sugars,
past the gray unrumbling mill, across
the river, up the rootveined banks and on
through hissing tapestries of timberleaves.

Hairgrove thought, *It is the day come round at last,*
and yet the jeremiah joy was gone.
The justice of the state was like a page
of algebra that ciphered to an x.
But there had been a day five years before
when Eli Snyder sat in the Trading Shack
and malletted his words at a New York
journalist, swearing in evenhanded
strokes to kill Charles Hamelton forthwith.
Hairgrove had felt each one: they drove so hard,
harder than the rifle balls he'd borne
within his breast. *I'll kill Hamelton*
—three words that raised the blacksmith to his feet,
folding his leather apron round the arm
in bandages. He turned to add, *I give*
my place to Brown, walked out,
strung his mare, and headed for Missouri.
To pull Missouri topknot down until
he'd made his rendezvous with Hamelton,
riding into the hearsay air as straight
and black as a walnut bole, leaving them all . . .

. . . Deepwoods they rode, to where two uprights stood,
eight feet apart and ten in height, a beam

between, from which an iron pulley hung.
The noose-rope fed around
it, then along the upright where it tied
around a quarter ton
of anvils in a box, fastened beside.
Get yourself yielded, Griffith the Sheriff said,
roping up his hands. The Texan raised
his head, the beard grown gray around a web
of scar across his cheek.
By order of the District Court . . . the Sheriff
started. Hairgrove heard him halt, then start again
and read it through. He turned to place the hood.
Hairgrove dismounted, shed his moleskin coat.
He's yours, the Sheriff said, handing him the axe.
The old man ran his thumb along its face
feeling its callus rasp against the edge.

He walked between the prisoner and the box
of anvils, taking a stance beyond
the plumb of their exchange. He raised
the axe, judging the arc. He thought *And now*
to strike: Griffith stood without a sound,
hooded, anonymous.
His shadow lengthened, seemed to stretch its arm.
Hairgrove caught wind of smoke, spicy as a flitch
of bacon on a beam—even now

when pots of beans sent up their thick, mealy
steam to turn a man and team knee-bent
from breaking sod toward home, just as in that
   hour
five years before, so now, as that desire
for food seized the belly, Hairgrove swung
the axe. It soared like a steel and mallard
messenger that slit the eye and flanks
of sky before it buried to the bit,
and hellbound sent the anvils with the man.
There was a catching kind of breath that came
out of the crowd. One of the militia fell.
Hairgrove laid the axe aside. He let
the Sheriff help him with his coat. He turned.
I thank you, Hairgrove said, bending down
to reach the axe. *Keep it,* the Sheriff said,
it's yours. Hairgrove held the slate-eye in his hand.
There was a grainy nick along one side.
All right, he said, *I will.* He tied it flat
against his rifle scabbard; then he mounted
and rode through the knots of crowd for home.

But it was not the same, the old man knew.
Something about the crowd. The likes of troops.
That the sweep of mare's tails in the sky
and buffalo like clumps of scrub oak

had given way to plumb bobs and the rule
of sums. Who would remember otherwise—
that two posts and a crossbeam took a roof
of wattles just as well as rope. And how
you cut your first timber on your claim
and laid it in a brake. And no man
ever hewed a two-day chinkapin like yours
nor raised such notch-end beams. Only the man
who gives himself whole-hide to land can know
how absolute it is
to own. Or lose. *And it is ours,* he thought.
He stopped, remembering now the skulking, the
 night
calling at doors and shotgun greetings there,
and when they all were forced to flee to Fort
Montgomery, rolling themselves in blankets,
sleeping in lines of six across the common
bed, and then at dawn Clarinda boiled
a block of mush, and they had talked the clock
around, about the slavers, courts, their hopes
for Federal redress, when then a form
rose out of the corner of that bed, its white
beard sweeping the burry homespun, and stood
and raked the air like grapeshot with its words
driving them back to where all thought began
steel-engraving them with what slaving men
would do who lusted after ownership
of others, how they shot his son, and now

would take the saber to them all. They would,
and would again, a hundred hundredfold . . .

. . . *Brown. Montgomery.* Names like fading rock-
prints
of a bear that turned from the watersprings
and climbed along the slopes beneath his lair
knuckling slowly erect until he stood
looking back across the timbered mounds,
rubbed his back against a haw, and disappeared.
They're gone, the old man thought. He looked
along
the moundslope, past the woods. A southwest wind
was rising, pulling the viking maple leaves
like boats amongst the air. Distant, he could see
the sinews of their river, with her banks
greenshouldered still. *I guess we all become
just names,* he thought. *Hairgrove.* He took its
taste.
Marais des Cygnes. The thronging waters
and the clanging fowl. *Trading Post.* A heelhard
floor of beans and barter. *Then let it be,*
he thought. *Better that every generation
lose its name, to find it for some truth.*
What did they say; an Indian girl once sat
along those banks, sifting the sounds of day

to sand, waiting for her Cheyenne chief
to come and set her wild-plum heart aflower
and died with each day's attrition till she drowned
deep in the darkening water, and then
in the spume of breaking wave, its hiss and crack,
the two great swans emerged and slowly spread
their wings, gaining the air. That was the myth.
And now the land was ready once again.
It was the time. And it was time for them.